1000
Things to
Colour

Kirsteen Robson

Designed and illustrated by
Candice Whatmore, Kate Rimmer,
Laura Hammonds and Ruth Russell.

Which robot do you like best? Colour it blue,
then colour five of the others.

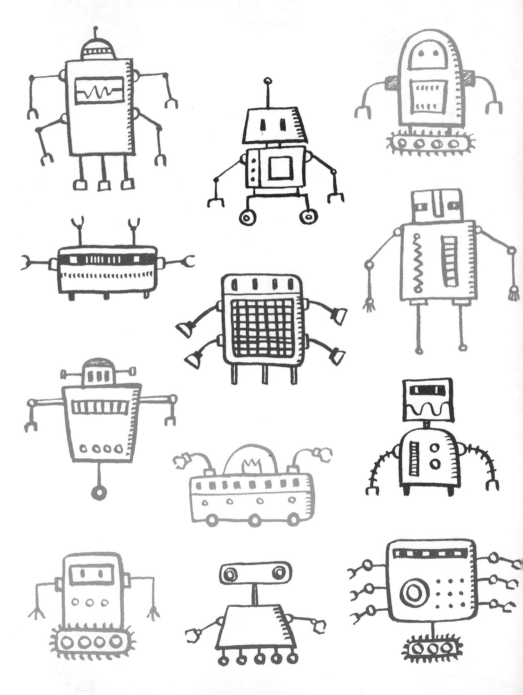

Colour three spaceships and the six planets
and asteroids they hope to explore.

Brighten up eleven bags.

Find seven striped gifts and colour them in. 7

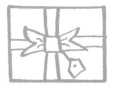

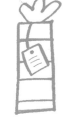
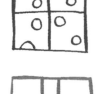

Colour two creeping
caterpillars and
fourteen busy bugs.

Four plain watering cans need brightening up.

Finish colouring the nine yellow party flags.
Then choose two more to decorate.

Decorate six plain cupcake cases and colour
five of the frosted flowers.

Choose fifteen vehicles and five other things to colour.

Give seven smiling kitties
multi-coloured coats to
be proud of.

Fill nine snazzy snail
shells with rainbow colours.

Make five of these tents stand out from the crowd.

Use your pens to turn nine
fish into tropical beauties.

Colour six things the chefs are serving in this sumptuous feast.

Colour in ten shoes.

Fill in the spots and stripes to turn fifteen of
these fading field mushrooms into funky fungi.

Colour the five perching songbirds and their leafy branches.

Fill in the tails of five little foxes.

Put the finishing touches on seven blankets, and colour the two cactus plants.

Colour five fresh fruits and five tasty vegetables.

It's a hot, sunny day. Give six sports spectators pink cheeks.

Triumph! Colour six trophies, medals and rosettes to treasure.

Add a splash more colour to each of these seven sailing boats.

Use your pens to give these six
exotic birds fancy feathers.

Choose three scuttling crabs to colour and three slimy seaweeds.

Add colour to these mischievous monkeys so each one differs from its brothers and sisters.

Add patterns to brighten up seven tortoises.

Fill eight empty jars
with all kinds of
jellies, preserves
and pickles.

Give cold, wintery colours
to eight baubles and warm,
festive hues to another five.

13

Colour in seven
kites shaped
like diamonds.

Fill in five flags and draw
emblems on four more.

Select seven skyscrapers and fill in as
many of their windows as you feel like.

Add patterns to eleven arrows and colour in five more.

Brighten up ten of these bouncing balls.

Choose colours for six of
these designer seats.

Turn four apples into Rosy Russets and four more into Gardener's Goldens.

Colour in eight piglets.

Decorate the four plain eggs
and colour the geese
that laid them.

Cover five geckos with
crazy patterns.

Use your colours to beautify
five fluttering butterflies.

Four slithering snakes need spots, swirls and circles.

Find ten socks and make them into matching pairs.
Choose two T-shirts and cover them in stripes.

Choose six suitcases and use bright colours to
make them easy to spot at the airport.

Use your pens to colour sixteen snow-capped cottages and four pointed pine trees.

Cover fifteen floating jellyfish with spots, stripes, swirls and other eye-catching patterns.

Choose ten starfish and make
each one a different colour.

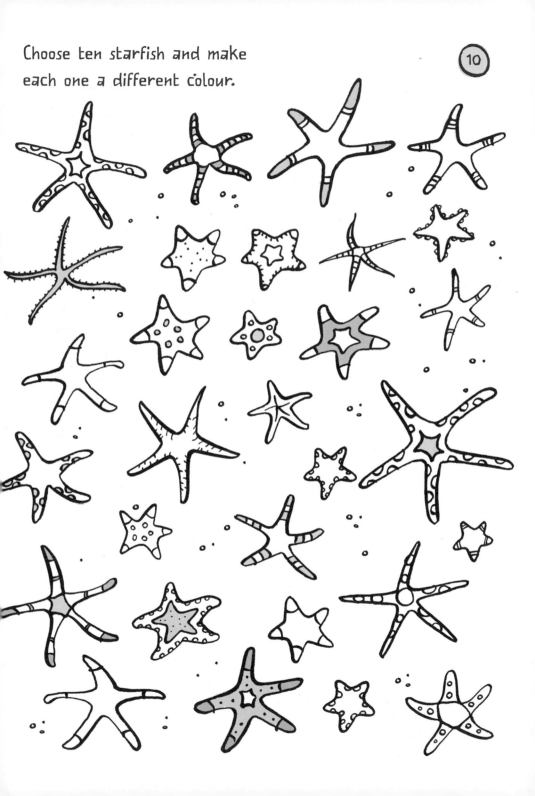

Will these five toothy terrors blend in with their swampy surroundings, or be spotted a mile away? You decide...

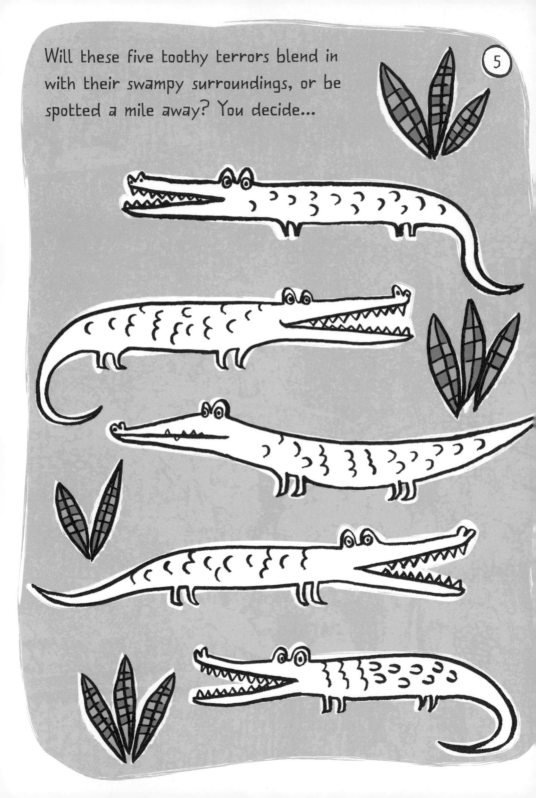

Colour these elephants, decked out in their finery for a festive procession.

Choose twelve winning designs in this stamp competition and use your colours to complete them.

Add patterns to the three plainest pens or pencils.

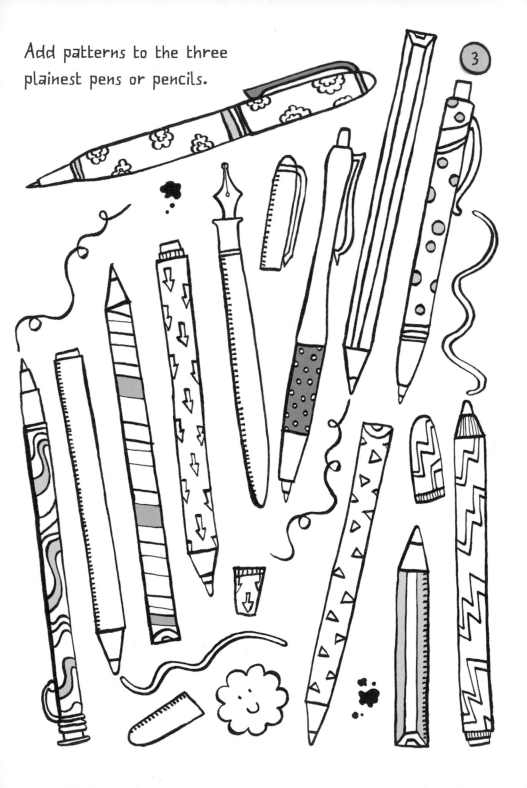

Give a new look
to ten tired old
lampshades.

Colour four cushion covers.

Fill in five pictures and five frames.

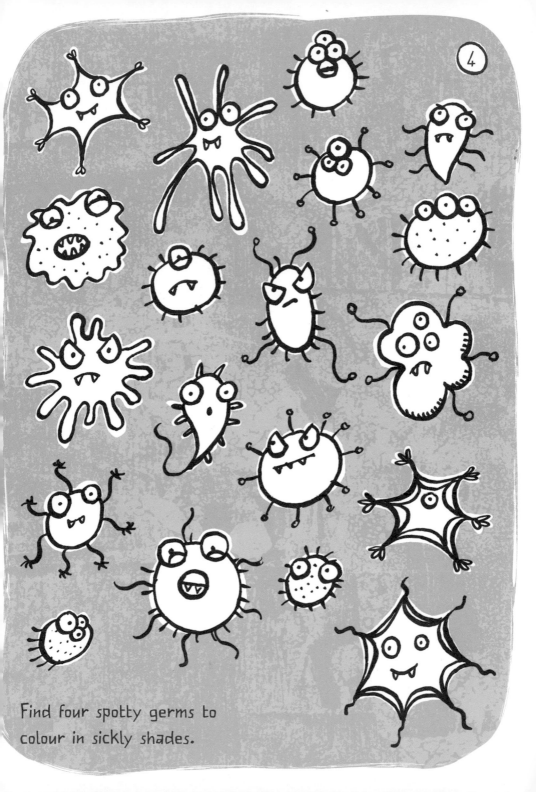

Find four spotty germs to colour in sickly shades.

Use reds, oranges, yellows and golds to fill
in the patterns on eight falling leaves.

Add colour to four busy diggers and two trundling trucks.

6

Colour twelve gloves and mittens
to make six matching pairs.

Add a personal touch to six winter hats.

Colour the details on ten tall townhouses
and six trees in the park.

Colour the stripes on seven sports shirts...

...and design seven pairs of socks to match.

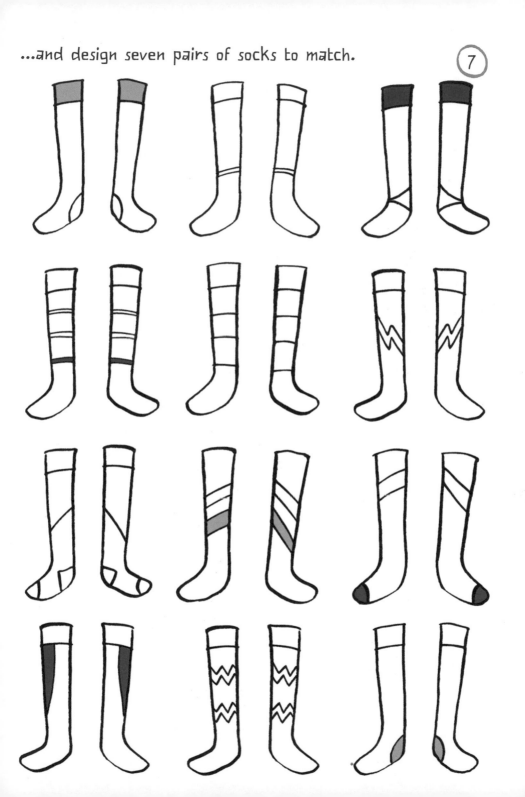

Give these six whirling windmills a fresh lick of paint.

Decorate the
parachutes.

Colour the windows
and portholes on
ten bobbing boats.

Give ten turtles super-showy shells.

Give five aliens
colours that are
out of this world.

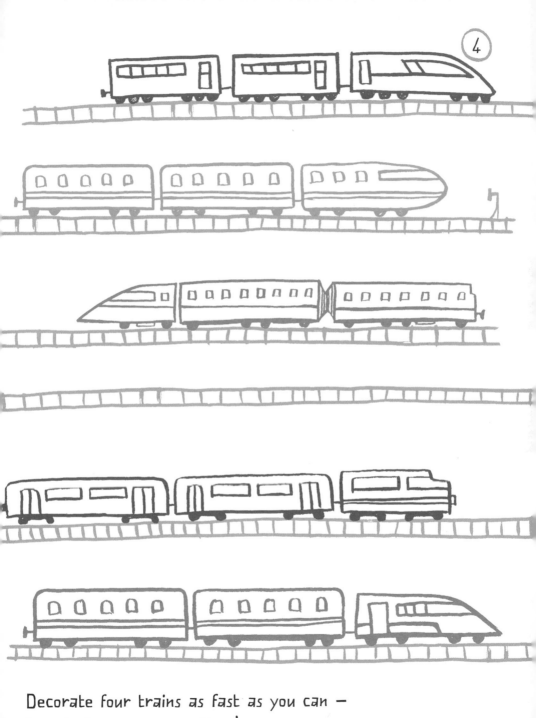

Decorate four trains as fast as you can —
but don't go over the lines!

Colour five rackets and
five things to hit with them.

Give six skaters stylish sweaters.

6

Thirteen buzzing bees need yellow stripes.

13

Fill fourteen bottles and jars with brightly coloured liquids.

Eighteen contented citizens are enjoying a sunny afternoon in the park. Pick something to colour on each person.

Give sizzling shades to eight buckets and eight spades.

Colour ten tools you'd
like for your toolbox.

Colour six splodges of
paint and show which tubes
they were squeezed from.

Fill in the details on ten
tasteless bow ties.

Colour the decorations on nine novelty hairclips.

Add colour to these
playful seahorses.

Give hats to five of the seagulls, and orange beaks to two more.

Shade in the stripes on the three kennels.
Decide which three dogs will live there
and colour them too.

Turn seven smiling stars yellow and
fill in four patterned planets.

Add colour to fifteen
fabulous rings.

Fill in three of these beaded bracelets.

Colour seven buttons.

⑦

Brighten up five
floating balloons.

Use your pens to perk up
six purple caterpillars.

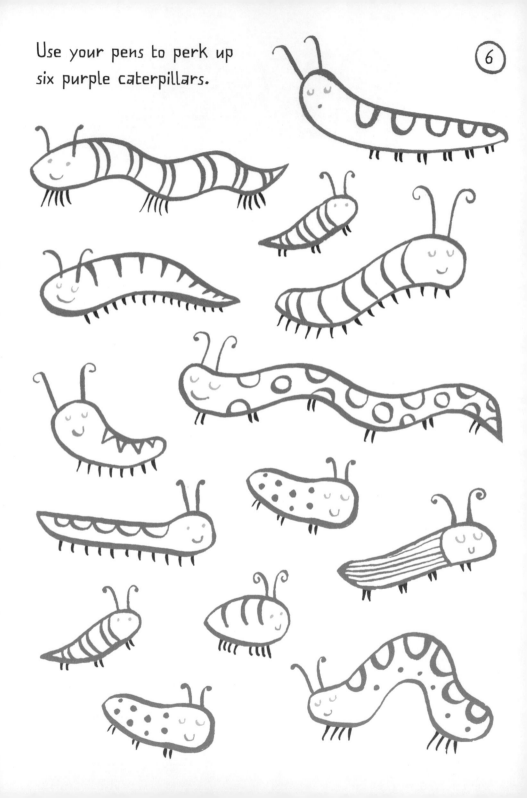

Draw patterns
on seven plain
plant pots.

7

Give eight owls a fine set of feathers.

Liven up the scenes in five of the windows.

Choose six creatures to colour. Pick whatever pens and patterns you like.

Colour the stripes
and flashes on ten
trendy rollerskates.

Fill in the patterns on eight yo-yos.

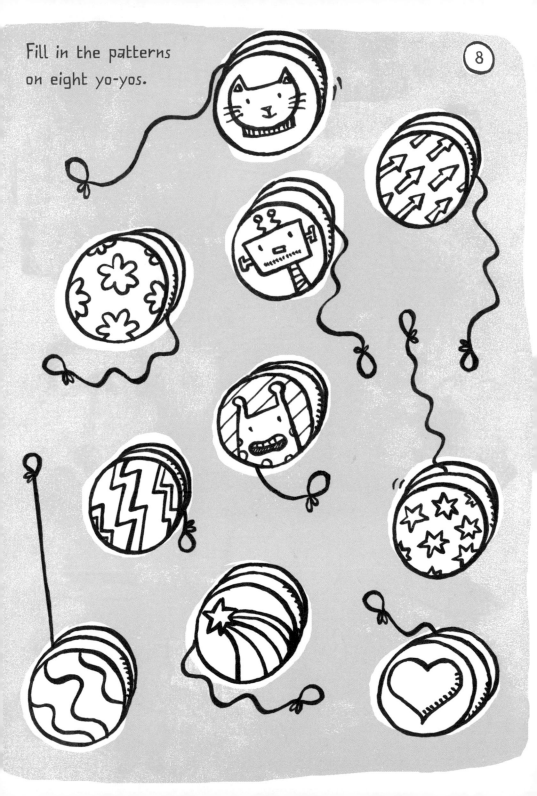

Fill in the details on
twelve costume hats.

Draw more patterns on
seven knitted scarves.

Shade in nine pairs of
novelty shades.

Use your colours to create eleven
irresistible ice lollies.

Make sixteen sweeties look
too tempting to resist.

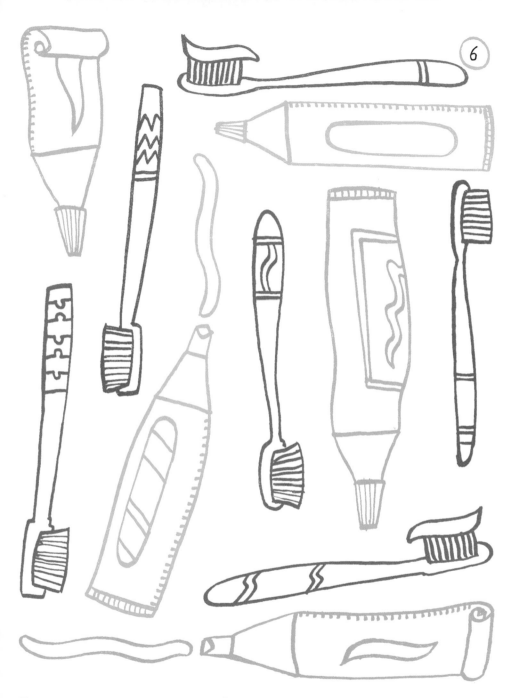

Design three terrific toothbrushes
and three toothpaste tubes to match.

Dress seven stagestruck penguins for a polar performance.

Draw watery patterns on
these diving dolphins.

Add designs bold enough
for planespotters to see.

Here are seven festival
balloons to finish.

Colour two people and two animals,
and add leaves to three trees.

Choose twenty bugs and
beetles to colour.

Colour seven sensational sundaes, and eight other delicious desserts.

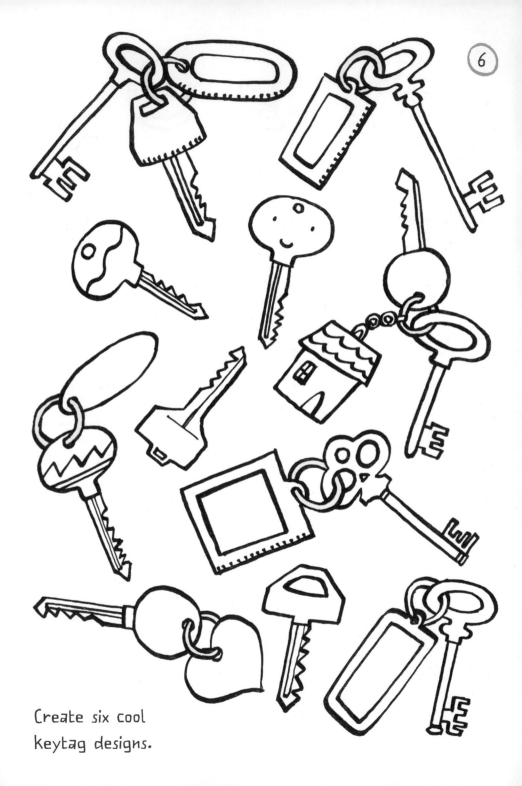

Create six cool
keytag designs.

Colour six prickly plants
and six patterned pots.

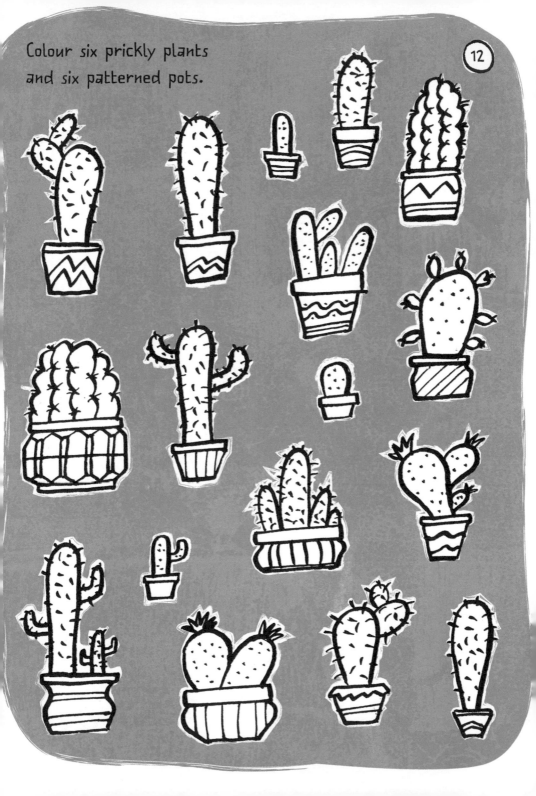

Shade in seven spiral seashells.

Colour in four
flamingos.

Finish the designs
on seven cups.

Add colour to seven
tempting cookies.

Colour six umbrellas.

Use your colours to bring to life ten cuddly toys.

Add colour to ten goggle-eyed monsters.

Make three thirsty
bats glow in the gloom.

Colour six beach huts on the sandy shore.